AWAY

A Children's Book of Loss

Written by

WP Osborne

Illustrated by

Ayan Saha

In the world of racial injustice and innocent deaths, our children's feelings are often left forgotten. Away is the story of a girl who loses her father. She experiences pain, confusion, and fear. This story shares how a Mother sets aside her own feelings to provide comfort and lasting memories for her child.

This book belongs to:

To memory of:

 Blessed are those who mourn, for they will be comforted.
—Matthew 5:4 (NIV)

Loss is tough, regardless of whether you are a child, teenager, or adult.

Parents, whether you are together, separated or divorced, you have a duty to be the ROCK. Providing love, comfort, and great memories are needed at this time.

Imagine the dad to be yours—what would you want? Love, hugs, patience, understanding, a calming voice, and memories.

How can you make this experience a time that the child can look back on and remember how you helped celebrate his or her loved one's loss of life during those dark days?

Rely on God's words for comfort.

My daddy has gone away. It is awfully hard for me to understand what happened to him that day.

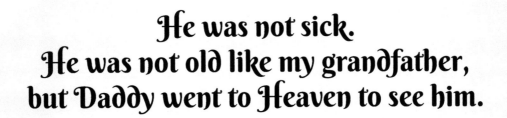

He was not sick.
He was not old like my grandfather,
but Daddy went to Heaven to see him.

He did not say goodbye.

Daddy was my favorite one to hug. His big arms went around my whole body. He squeezed and tickled me until we both laughed.

He put blubbery kisses all over my face. I used to
say, "Yuck," but I miss my daddy so much,

I wish he could blubbery kiss me again.
But no. I cannot see him anymore.

My daddy always prayed with me at bedtime and at breakfast.

Daddy said, "God loves you and will take care of you anytime we're apart."

She pulled back my covers and lifted me up;
she held me so tight.

She rocked me and said, "I know you miss Daddy.
I do, too. It's okay to talk to me about him."

Mom told me about Daddy's death. It made me sad, but I know why he did not say goodbye.

He did not know he was going to die; his life was cut short because of the color of his skin.

Some daddies are sick, some are old, some have accidents. No matter how a daddy dies, we miss him because he is away from us.

Now that I am a little older, Mom takes more time to answer my questions. She talks to me about my daddy every day. I used to have so many unanswered questions, but not anymore.

I now have many wonderful memories.

The pain is less every day, but I never will forget my daddy.

On Father's Day, we go to the cemetery.
We take flowers and lawn chairs and talk to him.

On his birthday, we take balloons
and play music.
I love to dance for him.

Happy Birthday
Daddy

For Christmas, we place a wreath on his headstone. My grandma goes with us too, sometimes.

One of the best things I have is photos. Mom has pictures of Daddy and me on her cell phone.

Mom surprised me and put all the pictures and videos of my daddy on the television. I can watch and hear him every day.

I close my eyes and I see Daddy's smile.
I know he is with God now. I can still feel his
unconditional love for me. I feel God's love too.

I will always be his little girl, today and forevermore.

My daddy is away in heaven with God.

The End

John 16:22 (NASB) Therefore you too have grief now; but I will see you again, and your heart will rejoice, and no one is going to take your joy away from you.

Thank you to my family and friends who have supported my dreams in writing.
Special Thanks to my girls, Teja and Liz!

About the author

WP Osborne loves God, family, reading, and exploring the world, especially Maui, Rome, Shanghai, and visiting beaches!

She also loves writing stories that encourage faith and lift others. WP is retired and lives in Illinois with her husband and she is often visited by her children and grandchildren.

She can be reached at:
www.wposbornebooks.com
Facebook: @W.P.Osborne
Instagram: @W.P. Osborne
Twitter: @WPOsborne1

Look for Mariah and The Red Monkey Series coming soon!

Win a Free Gift!
Find out how at: www.wposbornebooks.com